S0-BDG-012

Contents

In the Graveyard

Cindy, Grandad, Martin, Narrator

Martin

What was that?

Cindy

What was what?

Martin

I heard footsteps and something moved below the billboard.

Cindy

You're jumpy tonight.
We should have left
the playground
before sunset.

Martin

I know. But the baseball game was so good.
And my grandmother said she would come
and meet us. Sometimes she forgets things.

Cindy

There's nothing there. It's just an old
newspaper.

Martin

No, it's not a newspaper. It's someone! I
heard footsteps! Quick, let's run into the
graveyard and hide behind a gravestone! No
one will follow us into the graveyard.

Cindy

It looks like a ghost. We should never have come into the graveyard. There are ghosts in graveyards. We should have run anywhere but in here.

Martin

I wish I was somewhere else. I've got butterflies in my tummy.

Cindy

I wish I was safe at home in my bedroom, under my quilt.

Martin

Let's drop our backpacks and make a run for it.

Cindy

We could run to my grandad's workshop. The driveway isn't too far from here.

Narrator

The children dropped their backpacks and started to run, but the footsteps followed them all the way to Cindy's grandad's workshop.

Cindy

Grandad! Help!

Grandad

What's the matter?

Martin

Someone is after us. Someone followed us all the way from the playground.

Cindy

They followed us into the graveyard! And we had to drop our backpacks and run for it!

Grandad

Look behind you. It's Jake, my bloodhound. He must have seen you out there and followed you!

The Fisherman

Billy Townsend, Carmen, Grandmother

Billy Townsend

Please forgive me. But, do you have a strawberry or a pineapple?

Carmen

A strawberry or a pineapple? You look like a fisherman. Why would a fisherman want a strawberry or a pineapple to take fishing?

Billy Townsend

I need to catch something little and something big this afternoon, before sundown. So a strawberry and a pineapple would be good bait.

Carmen

Oh! I'll ask my grandmother.

Billy Townsend

Thank you.

Carmen

Grandmother. There's an old man outside. He says he's going fishing and he wants to know if we have a strawberry or a pineapple.

Grandmother

Oh! A strawberry or a pineapple?

Billy Townsend

Good afternoon. As your granddaughter said, I'm going fishing and I need some bait.

Grandmother

I don't have a strawberry or a pineapple. But I do have peanuts. I also have popcorn, grapefruit, watermelon, and coconuts.

Billy Townsend

Is that so! What sort of fish do people catch with peanuts?

Grandmother

They don't catch anything. It takes all day to get the peanuts on the fishhook. So people give up and chase butterflies instead of fishin

Billy Townsend

It is you, isn't it? It is Emma Greenstreet, isn't it?

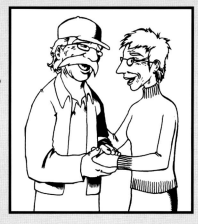

Grandmother

Yes, it is. And you must be Billy Townsend! It must be forty years since you and I played barefoot in the playground and made up that silly fishing game. Then you grew up and moved away. Where have you been all this time?

Billy Townsend

I was on a battleship in the war. One moonlit night we got hit. Nearly everyone was killed. I lost my memory for years. Then one day my head hurt. When my head felt better, I could remember again. I was homesick for Emma Greenstreet, so I set out to find you.

Grandmother

Well, you don't need to be homesick any more. Carmen and I will come fishing with you!